HANNAH
goes to
The Doctor

by Helen and Clive Dorman

Paediatric Consultant:
Dr Huw R Jenkins MA MD FRCP FRCPCH

CP Publishing

Poor Hannah is not feeling very well today.
Let us say hello to Hannah and the people who
are going to try to make her better.

Hello Hannah and Teddy.

Hello Rekha.
Rekha is the pharmacist's
assistant.

Hello Suresh.
Suresh is the pharmacist.

Hello Jennifer.
Jennifer is the doctor's
receptionist.

Hello Doctor Parrish.

We visit the doctor when we feel unwell and buy
medicine from the pharmacy.
Let us turn the pages and find out how the doctor and
the pharmacist helped Hannah today.

1 Hannah has woken up early today.
   She does not feel very well.
   She feels frightened and calls for her mummy.

Do you remember when you have been ill?
Were you frightened? Was it because you did not
understand why you felt like that?

2 She sits up in bed.
She has a headache.

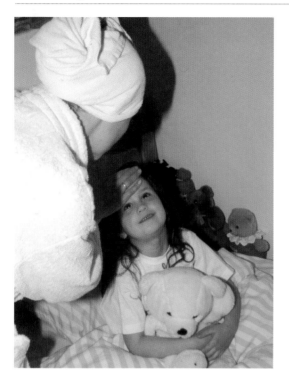 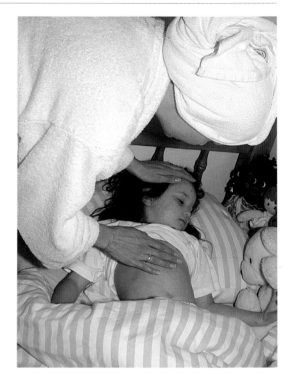

1 Mummy is feeling Hannah's forehead to see if it is hot.

2 Mummy is looking at Hannah's chest to see if she has a rash.

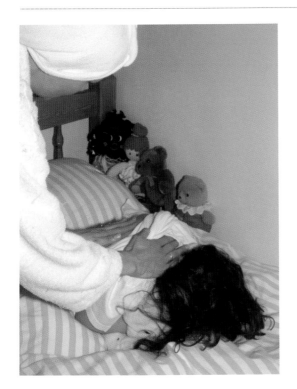

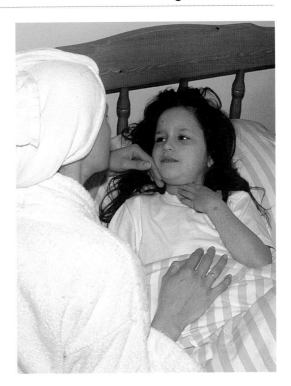

3 Next she looks at Hannah's back to see if there is a rash there.

4 Hannah is telling mummy her throat hurts and so does her head.

1 Mummy has gone to the bathroom and unlocked the medicine cupboard to get out the thermometer.

2 Afterwards, she locks up the medicine cupboard and removes the key. Medicines have to be kept in a safe place as they can be very dangerous if taken when not needed.

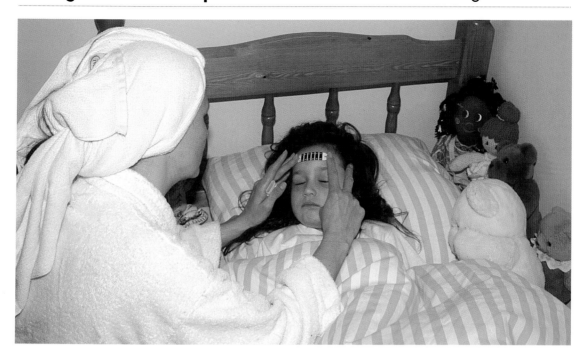

1 Mummy places the thermometer on Hannah's forehead
   to check her temperature.
   If Hannah is well it will read 37°C.
   Today it is 39°C, which is high.

2 Hannah's mummy is worried.
   She decides to telephone the
   surgery and make an appointment
   to see the doctor.

There are lots of different ways to take someone's temperature.
Do you know any more?

1 Hannah's mummy is
carrying her into
the doctor's.

2 Jennifer, the doctor's receptionist, is checking-in
Hannah with her mummy.

Hannah is in the waiting room with her mummy.
The waiting room is where people stay until they hear the receptionist call out their name.
Then, it is their turn to see the doctor.
Hannah's mummy shows her a book, but Hannah is not interested. She is feeling too poorly to read.

1   Hannah's name has been called.
She can now go with her mummy to see the doctor in his surgery.

2   Hannah's doctor is called Doctor Parrish.
Mummy helps explain to the doctor what Hannah is feeling.
Hannah is hugging Teddy for comfort.

1 First, Doctor Parrish takes
Hannah's temperature.
He sees it is a little high.

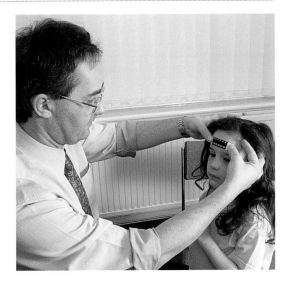

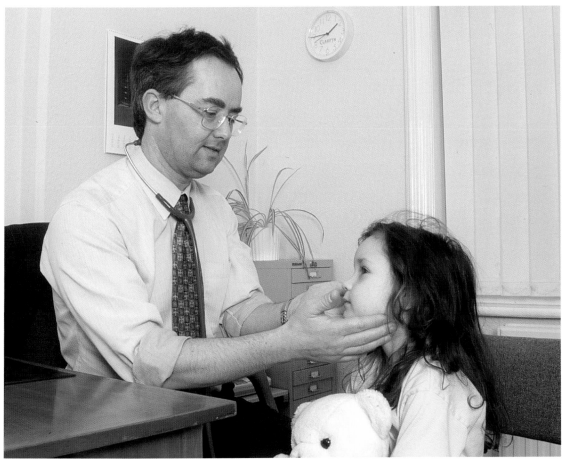

2 He then feels the glands by Hannah's neck.
Sometimes they swell up.
Glands help fight illness.

1 Hannah tells the doctor where her throat is sore.

2 He shines a torch so he can see better.

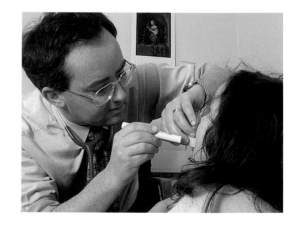

3 Doctor Parrish uses a wooden tool to hold Hannah's cheeks and tongue out of the way.

4 He can see little yellow spots at the back of Hannah's throat.
That is why it is sore, he tells her.

5 He first looks into Hannah's left ear.
He uses a torch which has a magnifying glass.

6 Dr Parrish can see deep inside her right ear.
Poor Hannah's ear looks red. It has an infection.

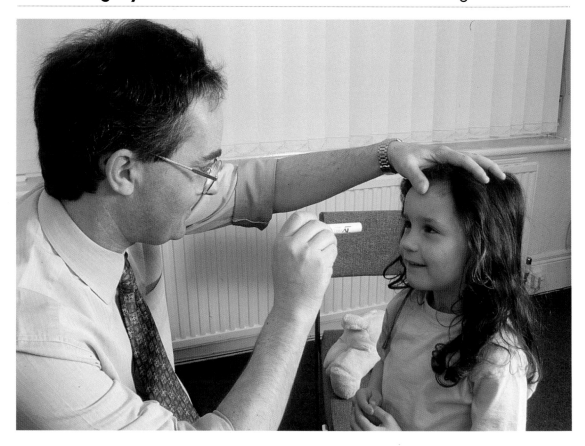

1 Doctor Parrish shines a torch into Hannah's eyes to see how they respond.

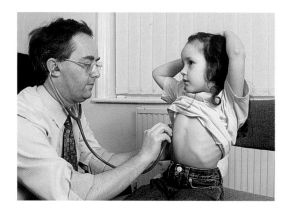

2 Next he uses a stethoscope to listen to her chest. First on her right side ...

3 ... then in the centre of her chest.

4 Next Doctor Parrish listens to the left side of her chest.

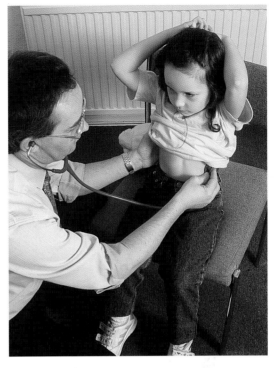

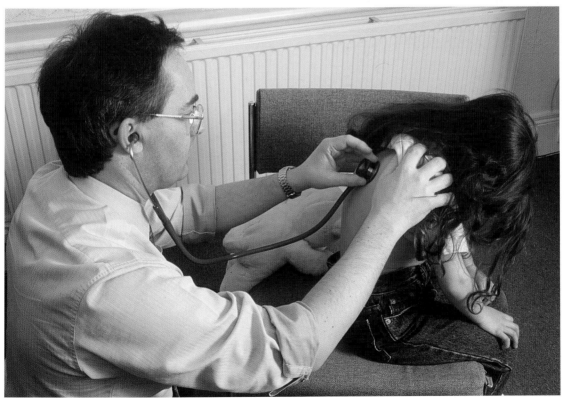

5 ... and finally her back. Sometimes the doctor may ask you to cough.

1 Doctor Parrish thought it would be good to check Hannah's weight.
But look, Teddy got on the scales first!

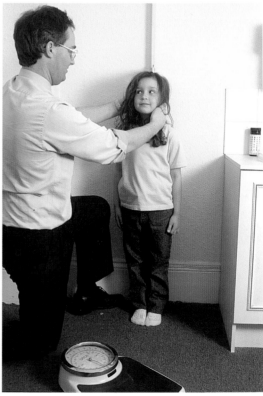

2 Now it is Hannah's turn.

3 Her height is then measured.

Do you know how tall you are?

Do you know how much you weigh?

4 Doctor Parrish has finished his examination of Hannah.
He is explaining to Hannah and her mummy that she
has an infection in her throat and ear.
Hannah will need to take some medicine to make
it better.

Have you ever had to take medicine?

1 Doctor Parrish writes out a prescription. A prescription is for the medicine Hannah has to take to get better.

2 He gives the prescription to Hannah's mummy.

3 Doctor Parrish says goodbye to Hannah and her
mummy.
He is sure Hannah will soon feel better when she
takes her medicine.

1 Mummy and Hannah leave the doctor's surgery. They need to go to the pharmacy to get her medicine.

2 In the pharmacy, mummy gives Rakha the prescription. Rakha will give the prescription to Suresh the pharmacist, so he can make up the medicine.

3 Suresh has finished making up the medicine. He is explaining to Hannah and her mummy how much medicine to take and when to take it.

1 Time for medicine.
Teddy has his first.
Well done Teddy!

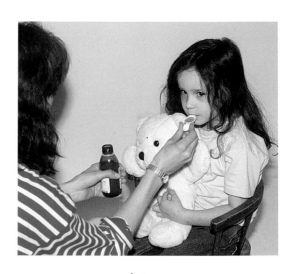

2 It is Hannah's turn.
She is not sure what it
will taste like.

3 Hannah finishes the
spoonful of medicine.

4 Mummy gives Hannah a
kiss to say 'well done!'

Hannah is now asleep.
She needs to sleep so that she will feel better tomorrow.
Sweet dreams, Hannah and Teddy!

Dr Parrish says, 'safety in the home is very important. There are simple rules we all need to know to help prevent accidents.'

Protect
Wear a helmet when cycling.

Lock
Keep medicines locked safely away.

Smother
Keep a fire blanket in the kitchen.

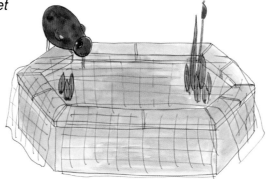

Fill, fence or cover
Make sure the pond is safe.

Cushion
Protect small fingers from being squashed.

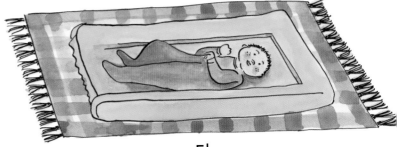

Check
Use a bath thermometer.

Floor
Change nappies and play with baby on the floor.

Listen
Use a baby alarm.

Shut
Always keep gates, doors and windows closed.

Block
Keep little ones away from stairs and the kitchen.

Smell
Fit a smoke detector.

Strap
In the car and the high chair.

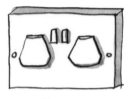

Cover
Fit plug blanks.

Tidy
Put toys away so that we do not trip up.

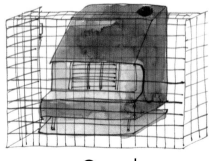

Guard
Where there is a fire, use a guard.

Dr Parrish says, 'sometimes when we are poorly we have spots on our skin. These are called rashes. Let us look at what these spots could be. You may get some as Hannah has.'

- Hannah has had chickenpox. She had spots on her face and the rest of her body. The spots turn into blisters and form scabs before dropping off. They can itch a lot, but you should try not to scratch them as they can leave scars. There are creams and medicines to help stop the itching.

- Hannah has eczema. She gets a rash on her wrists and elbows. Eczema is an allergy. Your skin reacts with something, such as soap or cream, or with food you may have eaten. The rash is usually itchy and dry.
Your skin needs to be kept moist with special creams and soaps.

Here is Hannah with chickenpox. It lasted about 10 days.

- There are other spots and rashes, such as a cold sore (around the mouth) or thrush (in the throat).
- Hot weather may bring up a harmless rash.

Dr Parrish says, 'it is good to learn your phone number and address, in case you ever need help or get lost.'

If you need help, are hurt or get lost, see if can find a policeman, or someone in a uniform.

Let us practise what to say…

1 My name is …………

2 My telephone number is…………

3 I live at ……………

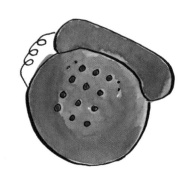

Can you name everyone on these pages?

Bye bye ... and ...

Bye bye ...

Bye bye ...

Bye bye …

Bye bye Doctor …

Now it is time to say bye bye to…
Hannah, who is nearly better, and Teddy,
Jennifer the receptionist,
Rekha at the pharmacy, Suresh the pharmacist
and, of course, Doctor Parrish.
Bye bye!

Your baby or child is unwell

It can be a distressing time when your baby or child is not well. You can feel helpless and frightened. Try to keep calm and in control: she depends on you and if you panic she will sense this.

A baby cannot tell us what is wrong. Even a child who can talk may be unsure what she is feeling or exactly where it hurts. She may be confused if she has not had this experience before.

Always follow your instinct; you know your baby or child better than anyone. If you think there is something unusual in her behaviour or health, seek medical help immediately. Everyone appreciates how vulnerable a parent feels at this time and often the parent's concerns are right, so check it out early. You will never waste your doctor's time. Ask the doctor questions – especially those you may feel are silly. By asking now you will know for next time.

Quite often parents are so concerned with their child's welfare that they find it difficult to take in what the doctor is saying. Try to get someone else to go with you so they can go through what was said later, if necessary.

Your child shows no physical signs, but is unwell

If there seems to be nothing physically wrong, but your child still complains of feeling unwell (e.g. headaches and stomachaches), try asking if anything is worrying her at playgroup, nursery, school, or when she visits friends or other members of the family, and so on. Children often find it difficult to say what is troubling them or put their feelings into words. However trivial we view an incident or what someone has said, your child regards it as very important and you should try to see their point of view in order to help. Children depend on us to make everything alright in their world and this often needs patience and understanding.

Accidents

Whatever has happened, the situation must be dealt with immediatelty and calmly. Your child may have done something you have told her over and over not to do, but you can talk about that when the injury is healing. Now she is in pain, frightened and needs reassurance. Act as quickly as possible, and ring for help if necessary or if in doubt.

Prevention of accidents

As your baby's abilities develop, so does what she sees and finds interesting.
- Be one step ahead and move objects of possible danger out of reach.
- Listen to your baby so that you know what she is doing.
- Put the changing mat on the floor when changing her nappy. Some young babies are very active and can wriggle off sofas and beds during a nappy change.
- Every day we use objects and do many activities that are unsafe for children. Children are natural explorers and scientists; they are inquisitive and love to learn by observing and copying. We sometimes forget they do not appreciate dangers in the home. When your child shows an interest in an object, teach her how to use it safely. Answering her questions can help reduce constant battles and possible accidents.
- Let your child have her very own box, drawer or cupboard which only *she* can open and close. Make it her special place for storing what she wants. This can be turned into a game so you have to ask her if you want to open it. This helps her to get used to asking first.
- We can drown in 12cm (5") of water. Teach your child to swim as early as possible. It is not only good exercise but an activity in which all can take part.

Useful things to have around the home
- A good first aid kit and fire blanket easy to hand.
- A basic first aid book.
- Information on child ailments and what to look out for.
- Relevent telephone help numbers by the phone.

First published in 2000 by CP Publishing
Richmond, Surrey, United Kingdom

Text Copyright © 1999 Helen & Clive Dorman
Photographs Copyright © 1999 Helen Dorman
This edition Copyright © 2000 The Children's Project Ltd

Illustrations by Nicky Plumbley

Helen and Clive Dorman have asserted their moral right to be identified as the authors of this work in accordance with the Copyright, Design and Patents Act 1988.

ISBN 1 903275 04 0

Printed in Hong Kong

Acknowledgements
We would like to thank the St Albans Medical Centre, Kingston-upon-Thames and Southcroft Pharmacy, Richmond, for their cooperation. Special thanks to Dr. John Parrish, Jennifer Rossi, Suresh Tanna, Rekha Tanna and, of course, Hannah.